Richard Scarry's
Great Big Mystery Book

Two favorite Scarry mysteries combined into one big book:

The Great Pie Robbery
and
The Supermarket Mystery

Random House New York

Library of Congress Cataloging in Publication Data.
Scarry, Richard.
Richard Scarry's great big mystery book.
SUMMARY: Detectives Sam Cat and Dudley Pig track down a thief in these two adventures.
Originally published separately in 1969 under titles: The great pie robbery and The supermarket mystery. [1. Animals—Stories] I. Title. II. Title: Great big mystery book.
PZ10.3.S287Rg   [E]   77-38512
ISBN 0-394-82431-8   ISBN 0-394-92431-2 (lib. bdg.)

The Supermarket Mystery

The Supermarket Mystery

Sam Cat and Dudley Pig are very fine detectives.
They will tell you that if anyone has a problem, they can solve it.

Grocer Dog telephoned them to tell them that he had a problem. Sam and Dudley drove to Grocer Dog's supermarket to see if they could solve it.

Dudley parked the car outside the supermarket. My! Where did Dudley ever learn how to drive?

CHECK - OUT COUNTER

Grocer Dog explained that someone
had been stealing food from his supermarket.
The only way out was through the check-out counter.
Someone had been sneaking food out of the store
without paying the cashier for it.

"It's a mystery to me how they do it," said Grocer Dog.

"Then we shall find out," said Dudley.
"But first we must put on our disguises.
We don't want the robber to know who we are."
     Sam and Dudley went into Grocer Dog's
private office.

Dudley always keeps disguises in his umbrella.
Whenever he and Sam want to look like someone else
they put on costumes from Dudley's umbrella.

Just look at that nice lady shopper coming out of
Grocer Dog's office! And what is that in her shopping cart?
Why, it is a sack of potatoes!
    You wouldn't know that was Sam and Dudley, would you?
Now don't tell anyone!

"Keep your eyes and ears open,"
Dudley said to Sam Potatoes.
"The robber is probably stealing
food this very minute."

"Cootchie Coo," said Dudley. "What a cute little
baby bunny! But you are much too thin. Your mother
should feed you more to fatten you up."
    "That's not a bunny, Dudley," said Sam Potatoes.
"It's a doll."

A few minutes later
Dudley said, "SAM! I have
solved the mystery! I know
how the robber steals!
Look! There she is now!"

This is what Dudley saw.
Can you tell which one is the thief?
Are you sure?

Dudley rushed across the supermarket.
He grabbed a lady's hat off her head and
smashed it to the floor.
"I've got you now!" he shouted.
"That's not make-believe fruit on your hat.
It's REAL fruit and you were going to steal it!"

"Just you look!" said the lady.
"You have ruined my new hat!
You think you're so smart! Here!
You just eat one of these REAL apples!"

Dudley took a bite of the apple.
It was not a real apple.
It was made of cloth.
And it was stuffed with feathers!
Poor Dudley!

Dudley was sorry that he had ruined the lady's hat. To show everyone that he was really a nice lady, he helped Mother Bunny pick out a watermelon that she couldn't reach.

"Now please try to catch this one," said Dudley. Meanwhile Sam Potatoes was keeping his eyes and ears open.

"Dudley," said Sam. "Did you notice? That doll is getting fat." Dudley was not paying too much attention to what Sam was saying. "Sam, look!" he shouted. "There's the robber! This time I'm sure of it!" Dudley ran off through the store.

A lady shopper wished to buy a sack of potatoes.
Sam Potatoes escaped from her just in time.
"That lady crocodile is the robber!" said Dudley.
"She is hiding stolen food in her baby carriage."

Dudley smashed into the baby carriage,
but there was no stolen food inside it.
Mother Crocodile was furious!
"Just when I finally get my darling little
babies to sleep, you have to come along
and awaken them!" she said.
"Dudley! Dudley! I could have told you
she wasn't the robber!" said Sam Potatoes.
"I know who is doing the stealing!"

And for once Dudley paid attention.
"Who is it?" he asked. "How do you know?"
"There is no time to explain now," said Sam.
"The robber has to leave by way of the check-out counter.
Hurry there! It's that lady with . . .

"...the fat—"

Before Sam could finish
talking— *Sploshhh!*
Dudley landed in a pickle barrel!
Klonk! Sam landed on his head.
He was knocked unconscious!

"How dare you call ME fat?" said the lady.
"And where did you ever learn how to drive?"
But look! Someone is picking up a sack
of potatoes to take home for supper!

Suddenly Dudley noticed that Sam was missing.
"Sam knows who the robber is. I must find him," said Dudley.
He asked the fat lady, "Where is my sack of potatoes?"
"A bunny lady took it to the check-out counter," she said.

Dudley rushed there, but the bunny lady didn't have Sam Potatoes.

Mother Bunny was saying to Grocer Dog, "I have decided not to buy any food today after all."

Grocer Dog replied, "But that's what you say every day, Madam."

Dudley took a closer look and wondered, "But how does she feed her baby bunny?"

Then suddenly he remembered what Sam had said earlier: "That's not a baby bunny. It's a doll."

And, my! That doll had grown very, very fat!

"STOP THIEF!" cried Dudley as he leaped out of his disguise.
"Your bunny doll is stuffed with stolen groceries!"
Mother Bunny was the thief!

BUT NO! It was not a mother bunny at all!
The thief was Blackfinger Wolf, the wicked supermarket robber!
He'd been wearing a bunny disguise. He threw his bunny mask away.

Out of the supermarket the robber fled.
Dudley didn't have time to look for Sam.
He had to catch Blackfinger Wolf all by himself.
Hurry Dudley!

Down into the lower part of town,
down where all the robbers lived,
Blackfinger Wolf rolled into his robber's den.
Dudley rolled after him . . .

. . . right into a trap!

Poor Dudley!
"Oh! I wish Sam was here,"
he moaned.

Just then the doll began to move and walk.
"HELP!" screamed Blackfinger. "The doll is alive!
HELP! SAVE ME!"
Blackfinger let go of the rope and started to run away.

Crrrump!
Dudley landed on top of him.
But Dudley was afraid of the doll, too!
"HELP! SAVE ME!" he shouted.
The doll stopped in front of him.
Zzzip!

Out of the doll stepped a sack of potatoes.

And out of the sack
of potatoes stepped Sam!

"SAM! It's you!" said Dudley happily.

"DUDLEY! It's you!" said Sam. "But how
did I get here?"

Then Dudley explained, "Your disguise
was so good that Blackfinger Wolf thought you
were really a sack of potatoes and stole you, too!"

"He was a very clever thief," said Sam.

"But we are very clever detectives,
aren't we?" Dudley grinned.

The Great Pie Robbery

The Great Pie Robbery

Sam Cat and Dudley Pig are detectives.
They find children who get lost.
They catch robbers who steal things.
Brrring! It was Ma Dog calling.
Something was wrong! What could it be?

They hopped into their car to find out.

Sam and Dudley hurried to Ma Dog's bakery.
"Where did you ever learn how to drive?"
shouted the policeman.

"Some thieves have stolen my pies," said Ma Dog.
Dudley looked through his magnifying glass for clues.
Clues are things like fingerprints that thieves leave behind
by mistake. Clues help detectives find thieves.
"Hmmm. There were two of them. I can tell from their
tracks," said Dudley. "Very fine clues to follow."

"Aha! Look there, Sam! The fingerprint clues go out through
that little window," said Dudley. "After them!"

"Please give me a boost,"
said Dudley.
Ugh! Squinch!

"HELP! I'm stuck, Sam.
Do something to get me out!"

Ooof!

"Dudley, LOOK! There go the thieves," said Sam.

"Aha! One of them has torn his pants on that rosebush," said Dudley. "Aha! They have left footprint clues in the mud leading to that car. THERE THEY GO NOW!" shouted Dudley. "I can tell it is them because they have cherry pie on their faces!"

Dudley is very good at clues.

Through the crowded streets they chased the robbers.

"Dudley," said Sam, "maybe we should let that big truck come through the tunnel first."

"Oh I can see that there is plenty of room for both of us," said Dudley.

Crrrunch!

"Now wouldn't you think that truck driver could have seen that there wasn't enough room for both of us?" said Dudley. "I wonder where he ever learned how to drive?"

"Come on, Sam. Hurry! We must catch the thieves," said Dudley.

Sam and Dudley needed a new car to chase after the robbers.
Dudley stopped a car.
"My dear lady," he said. "Please follow that car."

The robbers ran into a restaurant.
"Follow them!" said Dudley.
The lady followed them.

The waiter asked them what they wanted.
"Two thieves with cherry pie on their faces," said Dudley.
"I don't know if we have any thieves," said the waiter,
"but we do have all kinds of other people who have
cherry pie on their faces."

Dudley was puzzled. How would he ever be able
to tell the two cherry pie thieves from the others?
"I have a plan," said Sam. "One of the thieves
tore his pants on the rosebush. If we find a pair
of torn pants, there will probably be a thief in them."
"But we can't see torn pants if the thieves are sitting down,"
said Dudley. "How will we get them to stand up?"
Sam whispered the rest of the plan into Dudley's ear.
"You are a smart planner, Sam," said Dudley. "Let's try it."

Dudley went to a table and asked, "Pardon me, but is either one of you gentlemen sitting on my hat?"

The two gentlemen stood up to see if they were.
Sam looked for holes in their pants. No! They weren't the thieves.

Then Dudley asked Wart Hog and Baboon if they were sitting on his hat.
"No, we are sitting on our own hats," said Wart Hog.
They stood up to show him.
Sam saw that they did not have torn pants.
They were not the thieves.

They then went to another table.
"Pardon me," said Dudley again. "Are you sitting—"

Horace Wolf and Croaky Crocodile leaped out of their chairs!
Croaky was wearing torn pants!
AHA! THE THIEVES!
Before Sam and Dudley could do anything
Horace Wolf threw the tablecloth over their heads!

While Sam and Dudley struggled to get out
of the tablecloth, the thieves ran away.

They jumped onto a trolley car that was passing by.
Dudley caught the trolley car just in time.
Sam caught Dudley just in time.

Tickets,
please

Then all of a sudden the trolley stopped.
Horace and Croaky ran into their house.
It had strong bars on the windows and doors
to keep everyone out.
    Now Sam and Dudley had to think
of a way to make the thieves come out.

"I have an idea," said Sam.
    Dudley listened and said, "That is
an excellent plan, Sam. May I be on top?"

Sam and Dudley hid behind a telephone booth.
Dudley opened his special umbrella.
Why is it a special umbrella?
Because it is full of amazing disguises!
There are clothes in his umbrella that can make
Sam and Dudley look like ANYTHING!

Dudley put on the top part of the disguise.
Sam dressed in the bottom part.
Then Dudley sat on Sam's shoulders.

A lady hippopotamus knocked
on the thieves' front door.
"What is it?" asked Horace from inside.
"I have a surprise for you," said the lady.
"Come out and see what it is."
Horace and Croaky stepped out of their house.
They did not see the trap that the lady
hippopotamus had prepared for them.
"Where is our surprise?" they demanded.

"RIGHT THERE!"
said the lady hippopotamus.
Sam pulled hard on the rope
and those two thieves,
Horace Wolf and Croaky
Crocodile, were captured!

FRESH ORANGEADE!

ORANGEADE

TAXI

Sam and Dudley tied their prisoners
to the top of a taxi. They drove back
to Ma Dog's bakery. She would know how
to punish a couple of pie stealers!

"You naughty thieves," said Ma Dog. "For punishment
you will have to wash all my pots and pans."
"*Oooh!*" said Horace and Croaky together.
Maybe THAT will teach them to be good!

And she had an enormous cherry pie for Sam and Dudley. What a delicious reward!

"Here! Let me carry it, Sam," said Dudley. "You might drop it. Thank you very much, Ma Dog."

"Oh, dear! Are you all right, Dudley?" asked Sam.

Wasn't it lucky that Ma Dog had another pie to give them?

"You carry it this time," said Dudley.

Ma Dog waved good-by to the two great detectives. They had done a fine day's work.